MW00898551

Written by: Victoria Gorpin
Illustrations by: Stejara Dinulescu
Book layout design by: Emy Farella

ISBN: 978-0-692-15200-3

LEARNING MUSIC WITH

SNOW THE BUNNY

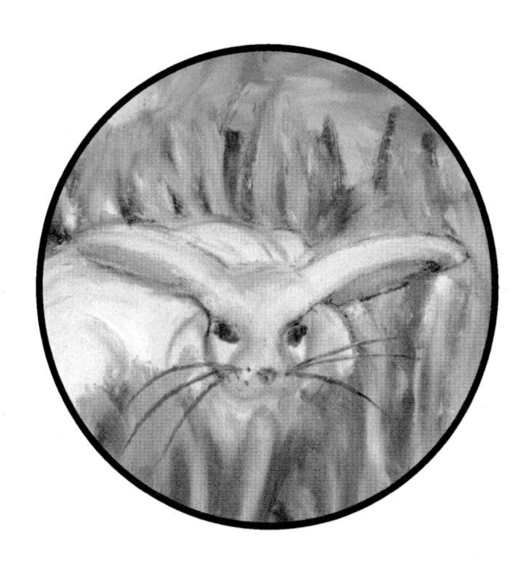

Written by
Victoria Gorpin

Illustrated by
Stejara Dinulescu

ACKNOWLEDGEMENTS

I am thankful to all my students, whose curiosity has impacted my desire to create *Learning Music with Snow the Bunny*. My goal is to make music lessons engaging, gearing away from the traditional curriculum, while integrating innovative activities to promote a natural avenue to learning basic musical concepts.

Children learn best through play and imaginative stories that they can apply to their authentic life experiences and expectations. I hope that each child, through his or her participation in music making with Snow, will use the character and story to inquire further about music learning and instrument play.

I want to thank my family for all the moral support provided and believing in my vision. Most of all, I want to thank my husband, whose companionship I value, for unfailingly encouraging my creative mind to share teaching strategies with other professionals.

AUTHOR'S NOTE

Learning Music with Snow the Bunny is created for preschoolers between the ages of three and six years old. The purpose of the book is to introduce young children to fundamental concepts of music reading, using iconic notation. There are three chapters in the book: the first chapter is the story with the melodies, the second is the iconic notation scores to be used for instrument play, and the third chapter has activity sheets for children to assess their understanding of fast and slow, and high and low sounds.

The book can be used at home for leisurely reading and music making or in music classes, whether private piano lessons or group elementary music classes. The story contains four melodies to sing along with your children or students, which is part of chapter one.

If a child or student has access to a piano or an Orff xylophone, use the iconic notation scores in chapter two to play the melodies on the instruments. The activity sheets in chapter three are intended to allow children to use their creative drawing skills and respond to the questions in the spaces provided.

ONCE UPON A TIME,
THERE LIVED
A LITTLE BUNNY.

HE WAS FAST,
A FRIENDLY BUNNY
KIND, SMART,
AND FUNNY

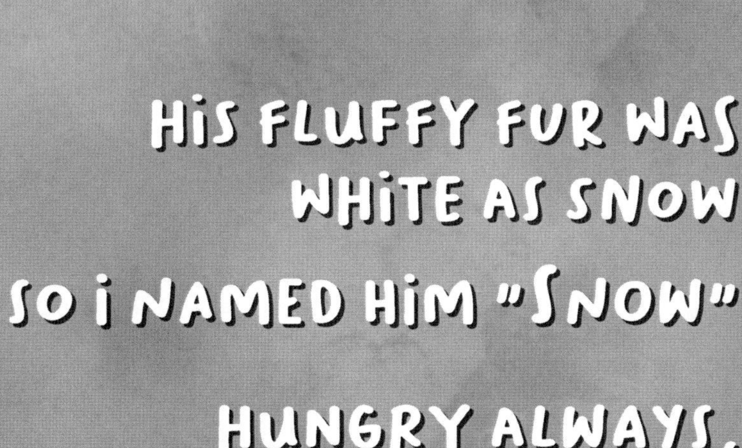

HIS FLUFFY FUR WAS
WHITE AS SNOW
SO I NAMED HIM "SNOW"

HUNGRY ALWAYS,
RUNNING FAST
SNOW WAS LOOKING FOR
HIS LUNCH.

Melody 1

♩=100
Hop, hop, hop scotch hop. Snow is hop-ping fast, fast, fast.
Through the bush-es, streets, and grass Snow is hop-ping fast, fast, fast.

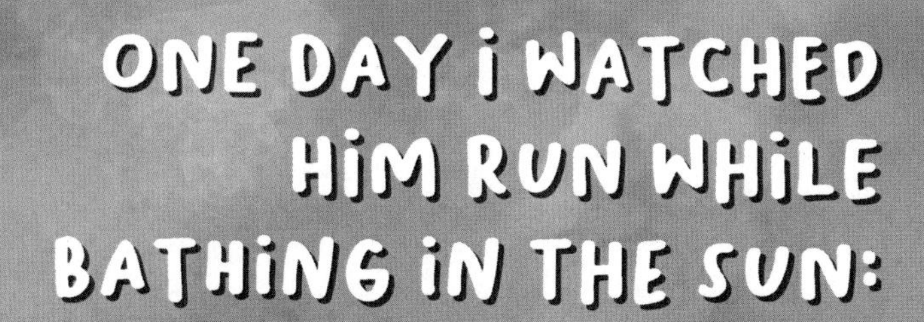

ONE DAY I WATCHED
HIM RUN WHILE
BATHING IN THE SUN:

TWIRLING, TURNING,
JUMPING UP, SMILING,
AND HAVING FUN.

IT IS LUNCH AND TIME
TO EAT, BUT HE'S NOT
SO FOND OF MEAT.

CAN YOU GUESS WHAT
BUNNIES EAT?

(WAIT FOR CHILD TO ANSWER)

Melody 2

♩=100
Hop, hop, hop scotch hop. Snow is hop-ping fast, fast, fast.
Seek - ing car-rots and green grass, Snow is hop-ping fast, fast, fast.

SUDDENLY, THE WOLF IS
HERE-
HUNGRY, GROUCHY, AND
MEAN.

THE WOLF SAW
THE BUNNY UP THE HILL
AND THOUGHT OF
TASTY BUNNY MEAL!

HIDING BEHIND THE TREES,
SNEEKING SLOOOOOOOWLY
IN THE REAR...

Melody 3

♩=70
Tip, toe, tip, toe: The wolf is com - ing af - ter Snow.
Think-ing of his yum-my lunch, he's a-bout to crunch, crunch, crunch!

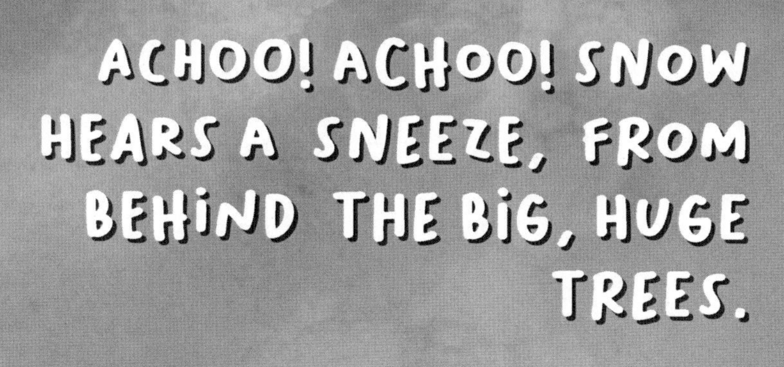

ACHOO! ACHOO! SNOW HEARS A SNEEZE, FROM BEHIND THE BIG, HUGE TREES.

HE TURNS HIS HEAD BEHIND AND SEES THE ANGRY WOLF WITH BIG, HUGE TEETH!

SCARED AND FRIGHTENED TO BE EATEN, SNOW STARTS HOPPING QUICKER, QUICKER!

Melody 4

♩= 100
Hop, hop, hop, hop, hop, hop, hop, hop, Snow is hop-ping quick-er quick-er
jumps a - cross the bush a - head, and the wolf rolls on his head!

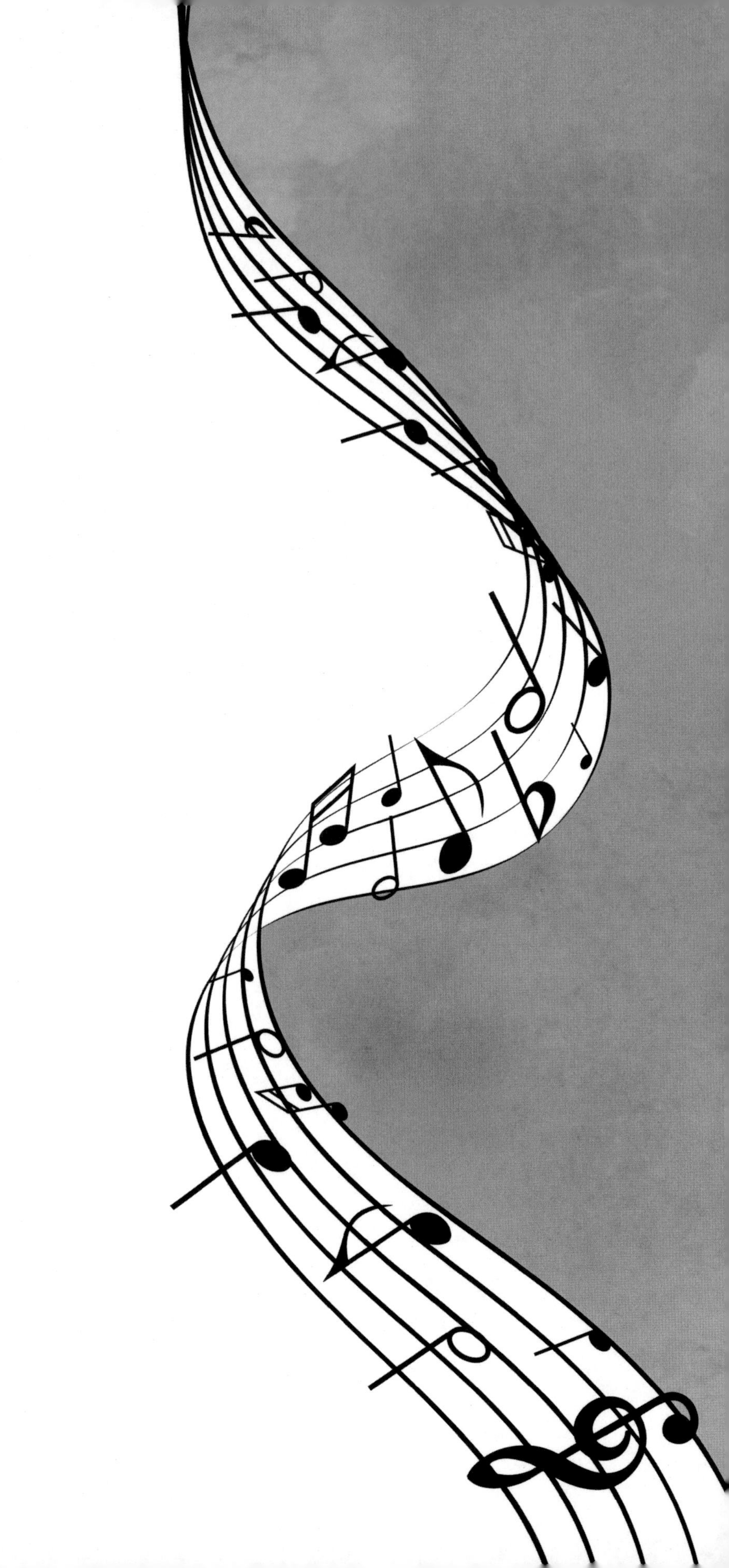

ICONIC NOTATION

TO PLAY ON THE PIANO OR
AN ORFF XYLOPHONE

HOW TO PLAY THE MELODIES ON THE PIANO

The bigger circles represent long notes (or quarter notes) and the smaller circles are short notes (or eighth notes). The five sounds are designated for notes ranging from C to G (C, D, E, F, G). Hence, the bottom first character circle is C, second from the bottom is D, middle circle is E, fourth circle is F, and fifth circle is G. Each patch of grass under the character circles represent a steady beat.

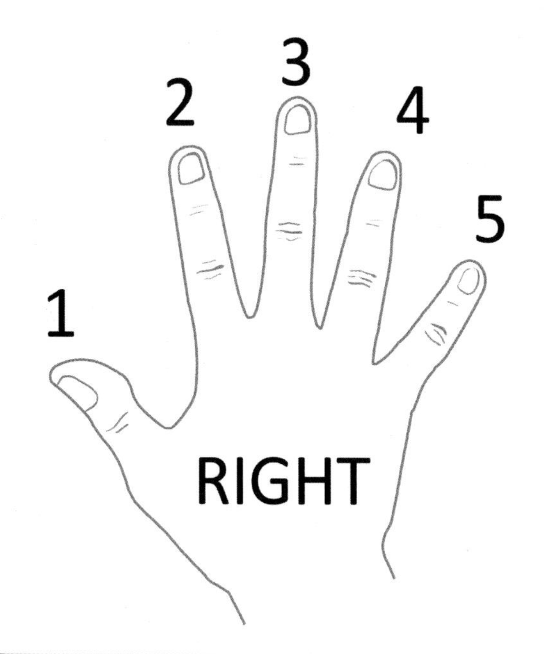

ICONIC NOTATION EXPANSION ACTIVITY

For an expansion, you can ask the student to play the same melody with the left hand, except the C will start with finger number 5. Please take a look at the second picture to see the finger numbers for left hand.

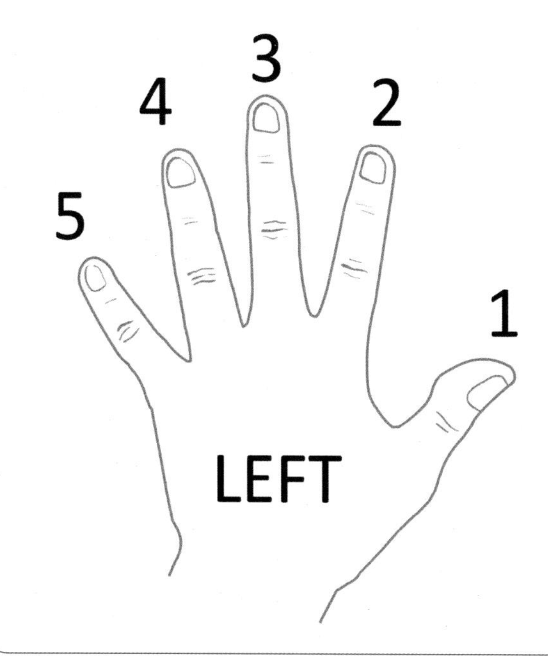

ADDITIONAL COMMENTS

The same notes (C, D, E, F, G) are used to play the melodies on an Orff Xylophone.

Melody 1

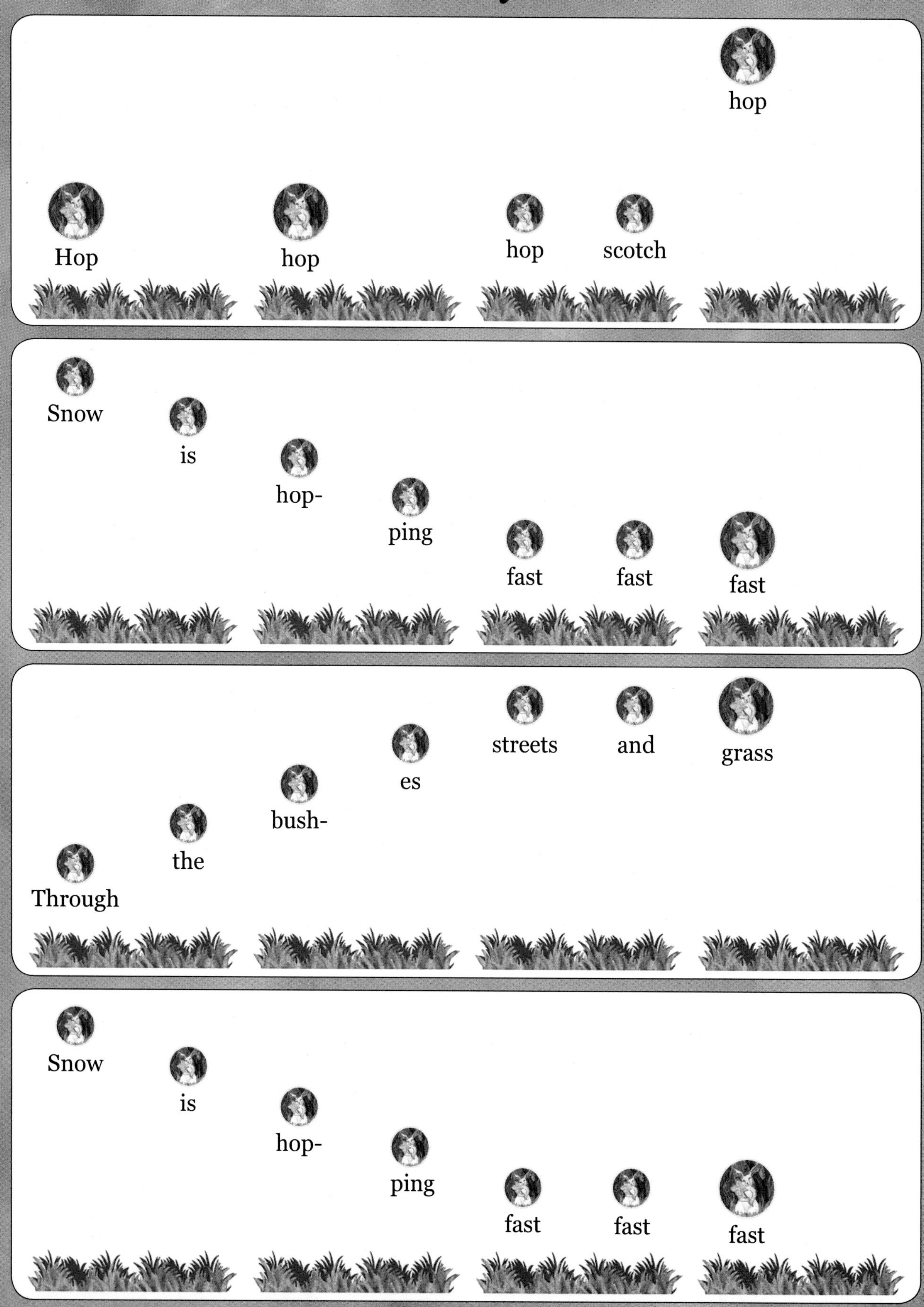

Hop
hop
hop
scotch
hop
Snow
is
hop-
ping
fast
fast
fast
Through
the
bush-
es
streets
and
grass
Snow
is
hop-
ping
fast
fast
fast

Melody 2

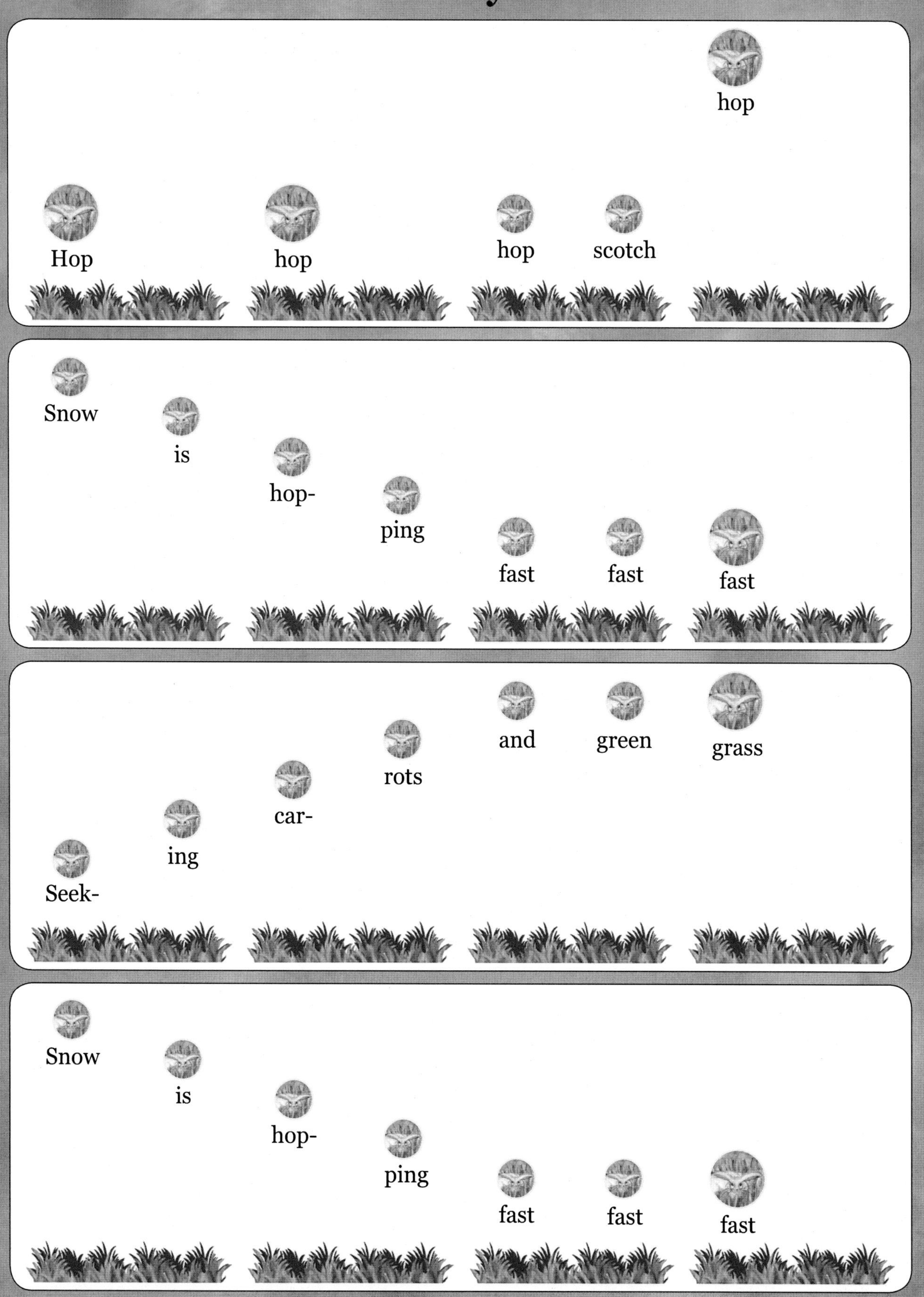
Hop
hop
hop
scotch
hop
Snow
is
hop-
ping
fast
fast
fast
Seek-
ing
car-
rots
and
green
grass
Snow
is
hop-
ping
fast
fast
fast

Melody 3

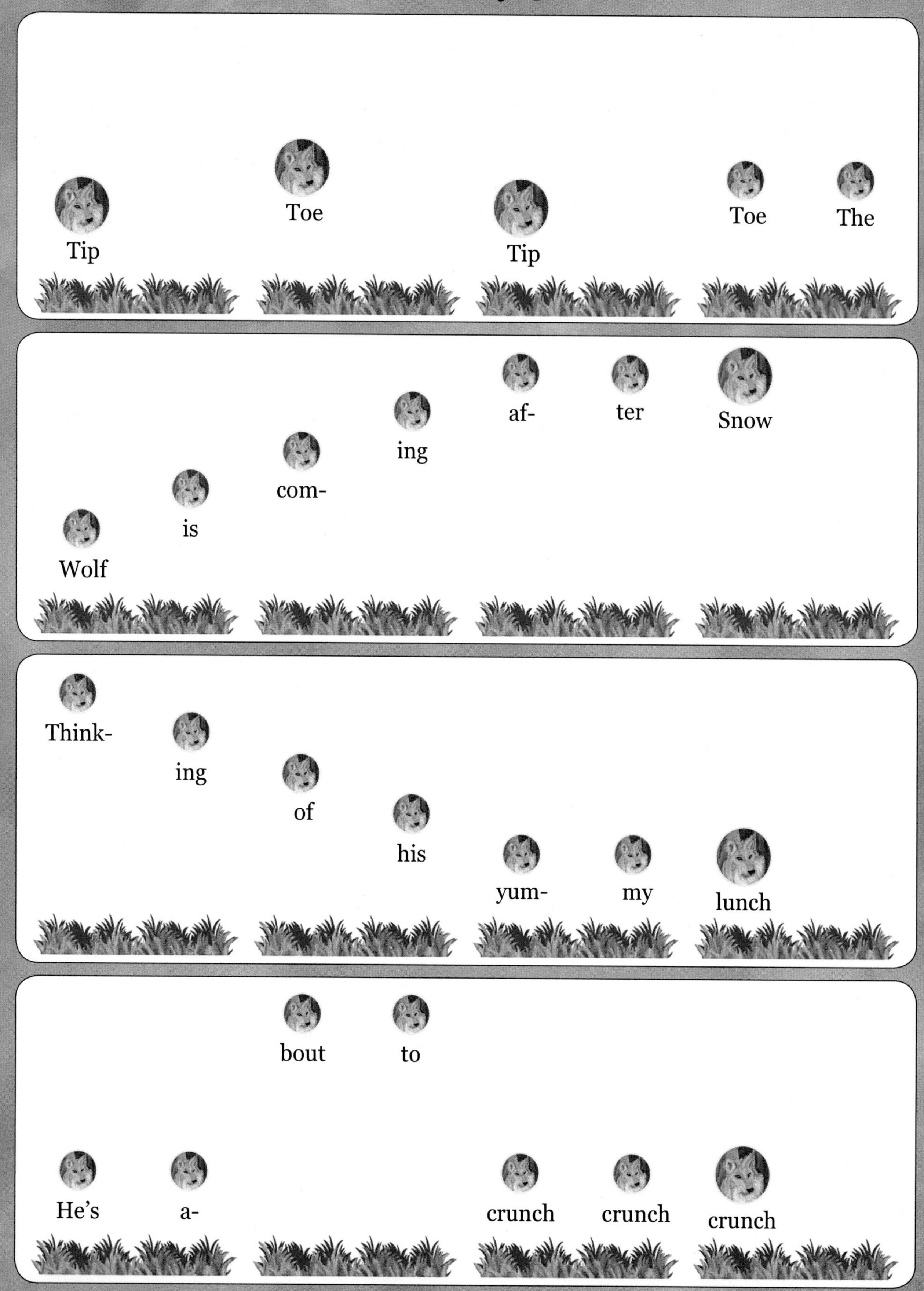

Tip
Toe
Tip
Toe
The
Wolf
is
com-
ing
af-
ter
Snow
Think-
ing
of
his
yum-
my
lunch
He's
a-
bout
to
crunch
crunch
crunch

Melody 4

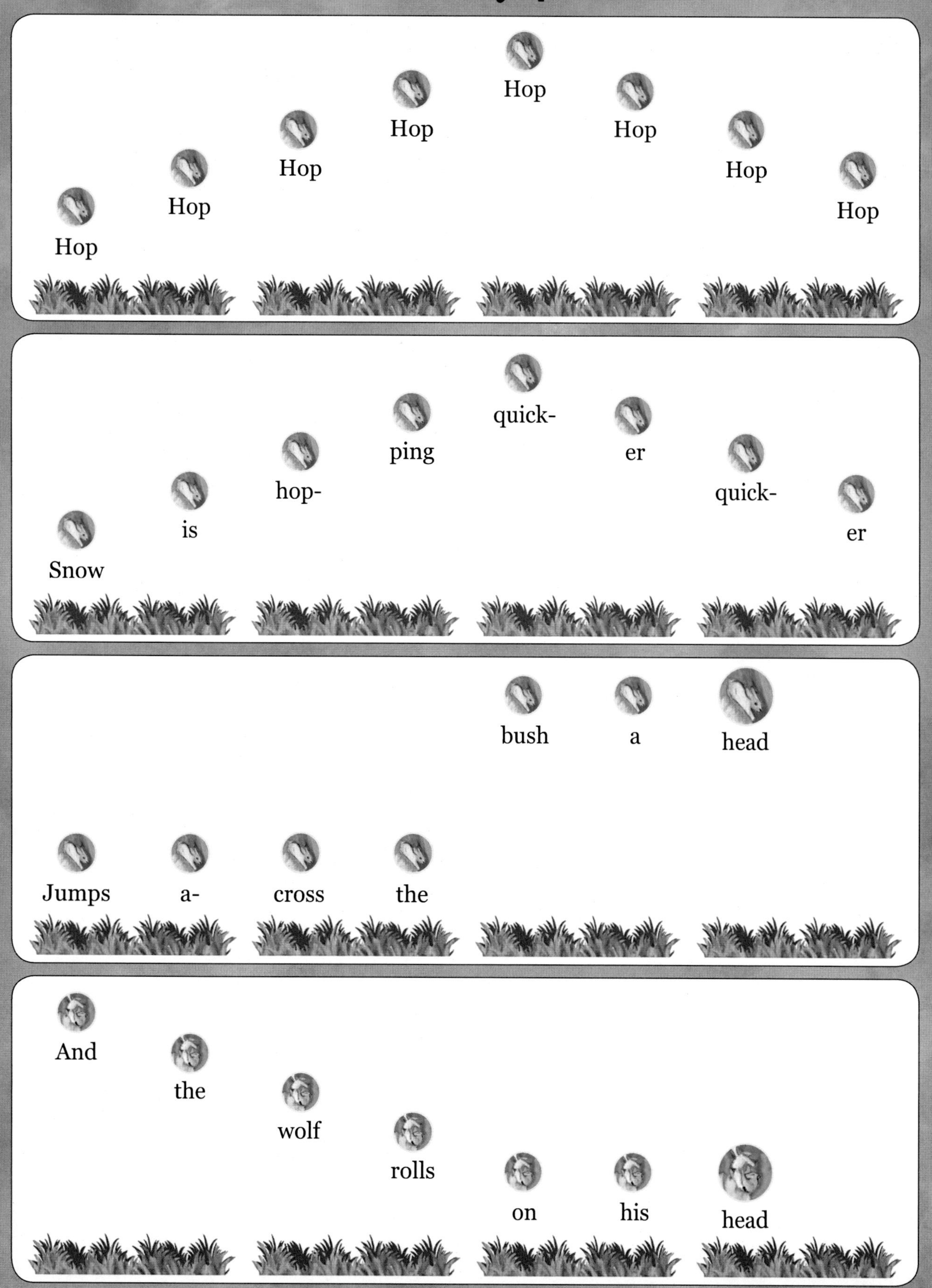

Hop
Hop
Hop
Hop
Hop
Hop
Hop
Hop
Snow
is
hop-
ping
quick-
er
quick-
er
Jumps
a-
cross
the
bush
a
head
And
the
wolf
rolls
on
his
head

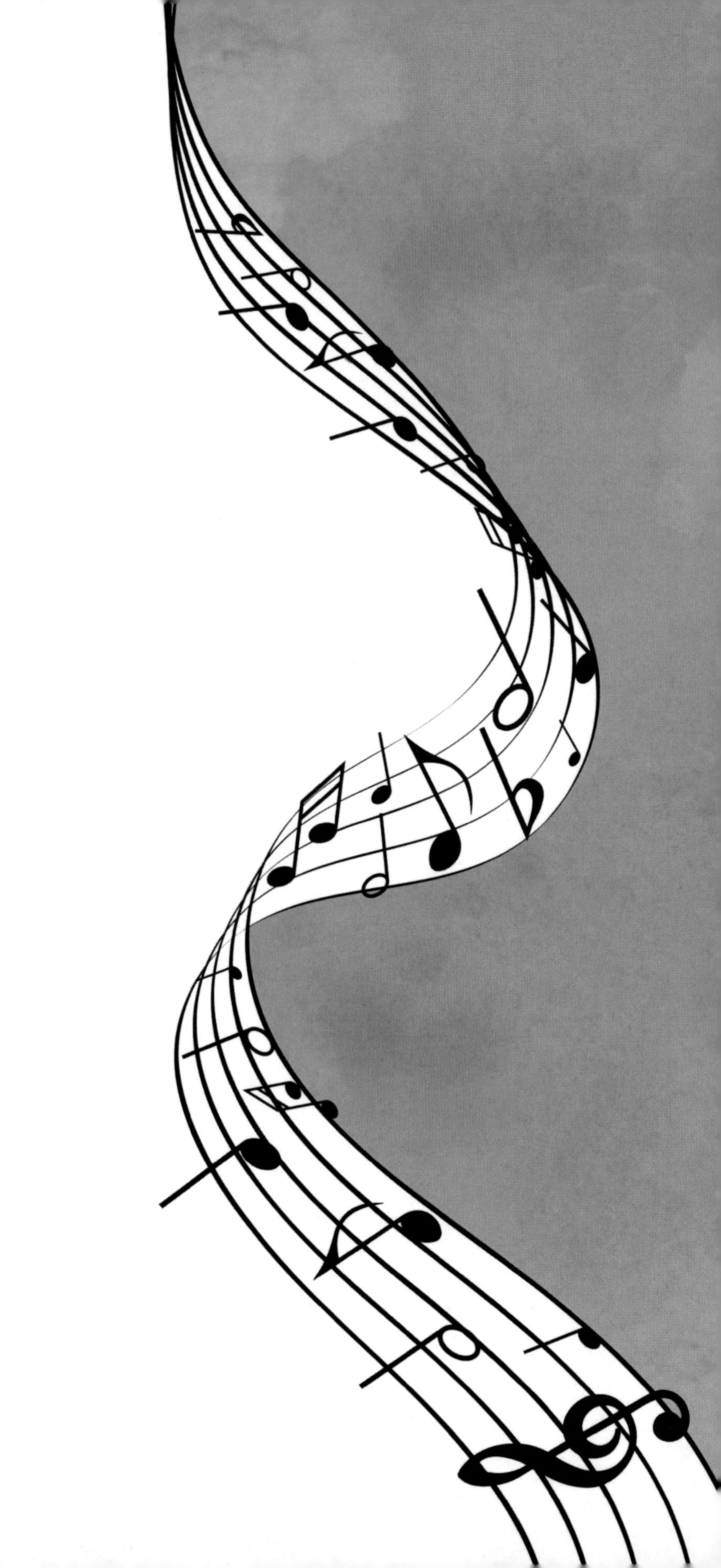

ACTIVITY SHEETS

ACTIVITY SHEET 1

(For oral skill purposes the teacher can play notes that represent sound examples in the proposed activities, on the piano. Ask students to play on the piano or xylophone what they have drawn in ALL 3rd and 4th activities.)

1. Circle the sound that sounds the highest

2. Circle the sound that sounds the lowest

3. In the space below, draw one low sound and three high sounds

4. In the space below, draw two high sounds and three low sounds

ACTIVITY SHEET 2

1. Circle two sounds that sound the same

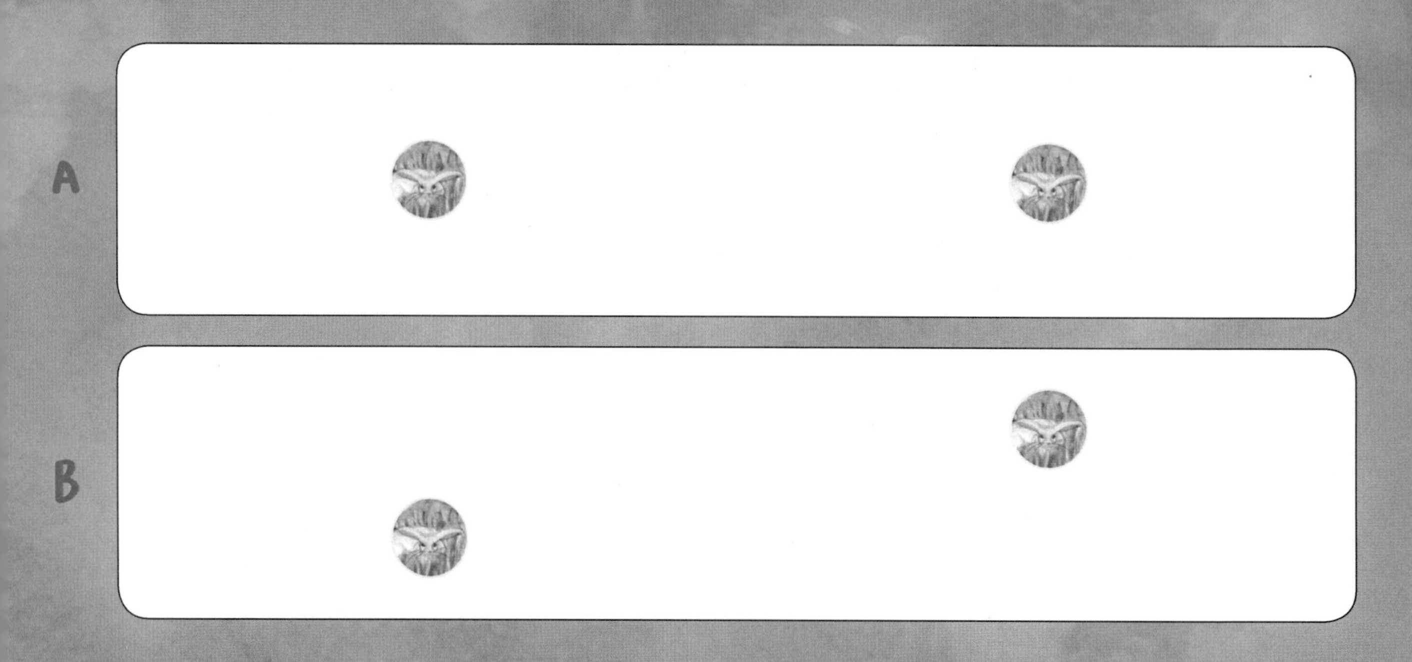

2. Circle two sounds that sound different

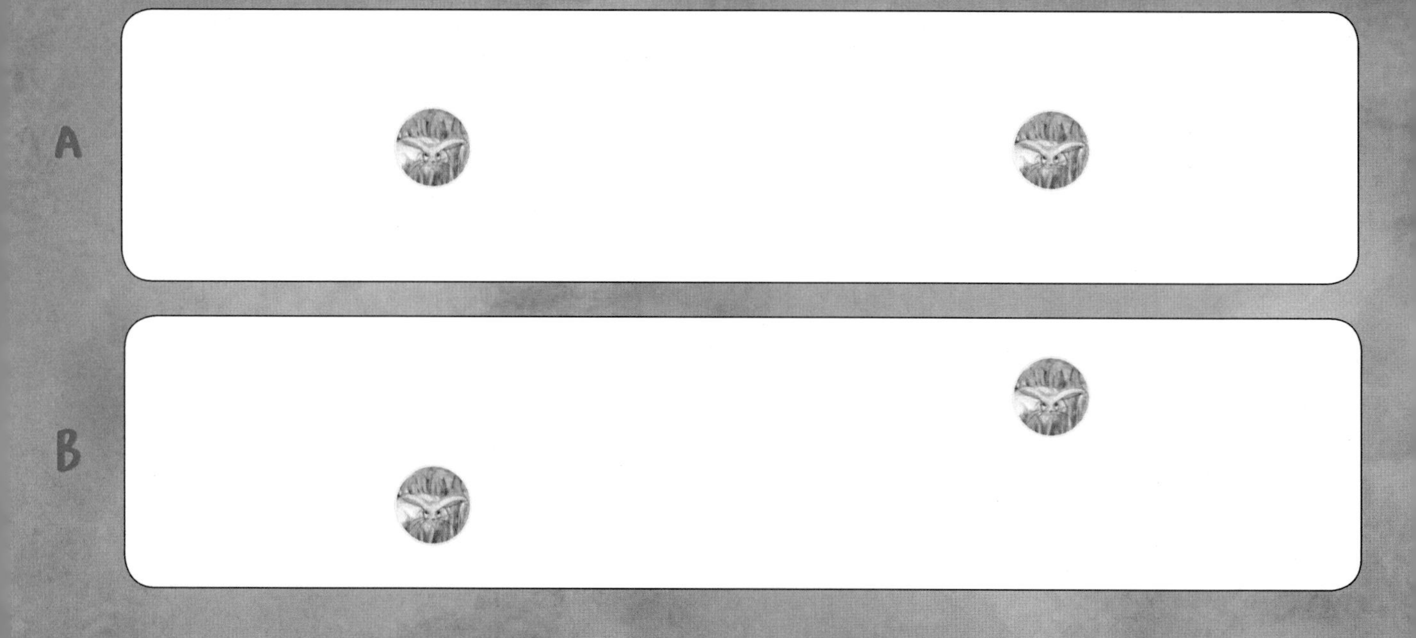

3. In the space below, draw three sounds that sound the same

4. In the space below, draw four sounds that sound different

ACTIVITY SHEET 3

1. Circle the sound that sounds the longest

A B

2. Circle the sound that sounds the shortest

A B

3. In the space below, draw three short sounds and one long sound

4. In the space below, draw two long sounds and two short sounds

ACTIVITY SHEET 4

1. Circle two sounds that sound short and different

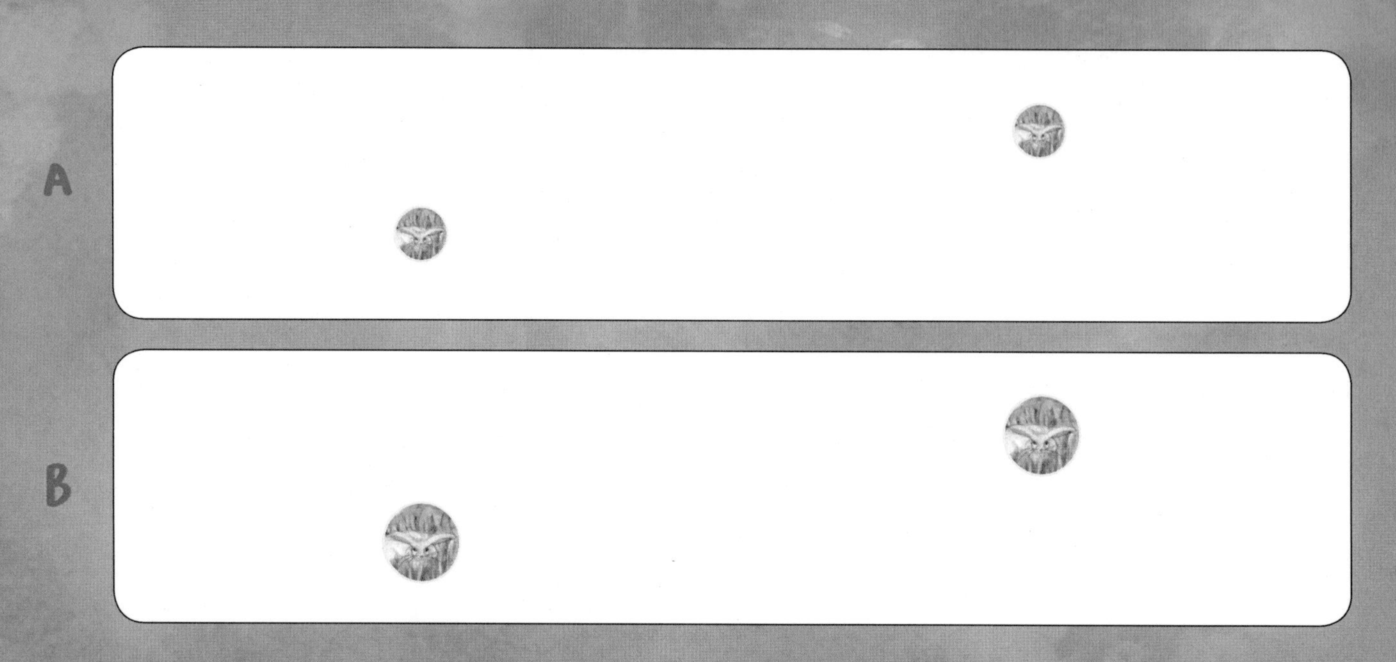

2. Circle two sounds that sound long and same

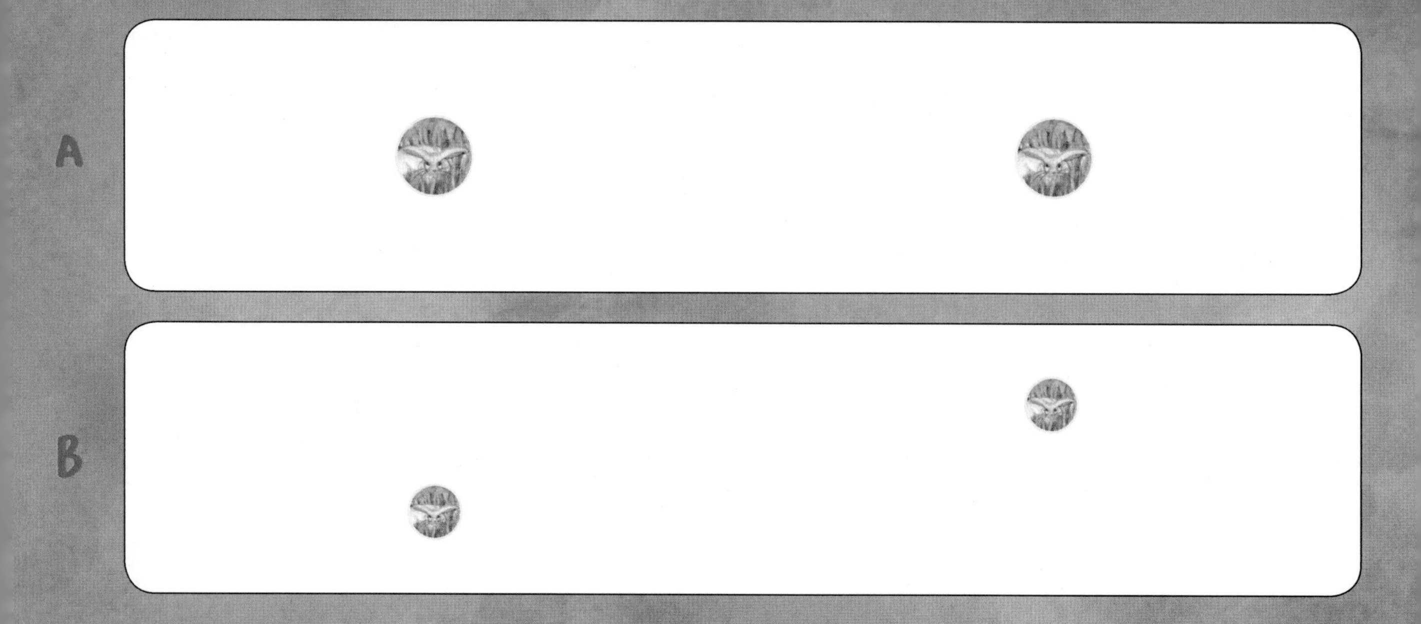

(CAN BE USED AS AN ASSESSMENT TOOL)

3. In the space below, draw three short sounds that sound different

4. In the space below, draw two long sounds that sound the same

Made in the USA
Columbia, SC
06 March 2021